TREASURES IN THE SAND

by
Perry Guy

Printed in the United States of America

ISBN 978-1-6319215-1-3

Acknowledgements

I would like to thank each of the artists for their great effort in illustrating the characters and their depiction of the particular scene.

Thank you so much, Bridget Starr Taylor for your Incredible work on the *Stuffed Pelican* (all artwork copyright Bridget Starr Taylor 2014). Thanks also for your amazing work on *The Beach Bunny, The Beach Mouse, and Dolphins On Parade* (all artwork copyright Bridget Starr Taylor). Bridget also did a magnificient job with the cover as well. It was a great pleasure to meet you on your stay here in Gulf Shores Alabama.

Thanks to B K Taylor for breathing life into *The Sandpiper* and a great depiction of the vehicle with the family traveling on vacaton in Various Northern States. (all artwork copyright B K Taylor 2014).

Thanks to Nancy Lane for her dreamy illustration of *Monarchs in November* (all artwork copyright Nancy Lane 2014). It made for a really cool ending.

All reproducton rights belong to the artists' and any reproducton without the artist consent violate copyright laws.

Thanks to Mary Teichman for her outstanding work with *Treasures In The Sand, Cotton Candy Skies, and Kites* (all artwork copyright Mary Teichman 2014).

A special thanks to Melissa Turk Studios in New York (melissaturk.com) for coordinating the efforts of the artist and facilitating the process.

Table of Contents

The Stuffed Pelican

The Pelican rested peacefully on the rolling waves
Content from a successful day of diving for fish

His plump tummy so round and full

However he still could not help

But conspire a gluttonous wish

Spanish Mackerel and Sea Bass are tasty indeed

And perhaps I have ingested

More than one bird should partake

But some crunchy Shrimp or tasty Octopus

Would certainly be the icing on the cake

However they do live on the very bottom

And Jester The Shark is known to harbor there

I am agile and swift above the surface

But below, no ability of escape if I should dare
Perhaps He would not notice one dive
Often it is there on the bottom He sleeps
I will scoop my catch quickly
Then my dining will be complete
So the Pelican flew up high and dove
Into the water straight down
So quickly to the bottom
And what a bountiful catch He found
Startled Shrimp and a School of Squid
Tried in vain to escape

But the Pelican was far too clever

And away He swam with all He could take

When suddenly out of the deep blue

Arose a horrific surprise

Jester The Shark appeared abruptly

And with a glow in his eyes

There was little chase

The Pelican was greatly out matched

To the surface arose bubbles and feathers

But not even the slightest splash

And although this story may seem sad

It is the natural way of life in the sea

And Jester The Shark did relay

That this Stuffed Pelican

Was the tastiest that ever could be!

Various
Northern States

License plates from Michigan, Wisconsin,

Indiana and Various Northern States

Stream down Highway 59 like nomadic tribes

Traveling to traditional Spring breaks

Granted it is just one week

But it seems to carry throughout the year

When snow mass and icicles

Attempt to suppress summer cheer

And it is in that one week

Birth of priceless memories create

Embedding smiles and sunshine

And there they will hibernate

Until released into converse

Smiting the bite of a cold winter spell

And propagate a warm aura of feelings
Through the fun stories that we tell
It is the bonding of the Family
That anchors these moments deep
And captures precious time in a bottle
To someday surface on that sandy beach

Traffic really isn't such a bother here on 59
As I drive towards home I contemplate
Michigan, Wisconsin, Indiana
And Various Northern States

Kites

There is something transcendental
About kites
Sailing up high in a tropical wind
Blue ocean as a backdrop
Framed by windswept quartz sand
Kites of brilliant color
Creative shape and exotic design
Gliding in a soft summer breeze
Graciously lend peace of mind
Kites imprint an endearing image
Availing on days when the sun does not shine

A romantic picture
Of a comforting place in a special time
Where the movement of the day evolves
On a slow summer pace
And the greatest priority
Is to make certain enough lotion
Is on the little ones face
Butterfly kites flapping in a wayward wind
An amazon parrot with a tail of tropical colors
That twist and spin
One with a patriotic red white and blue design

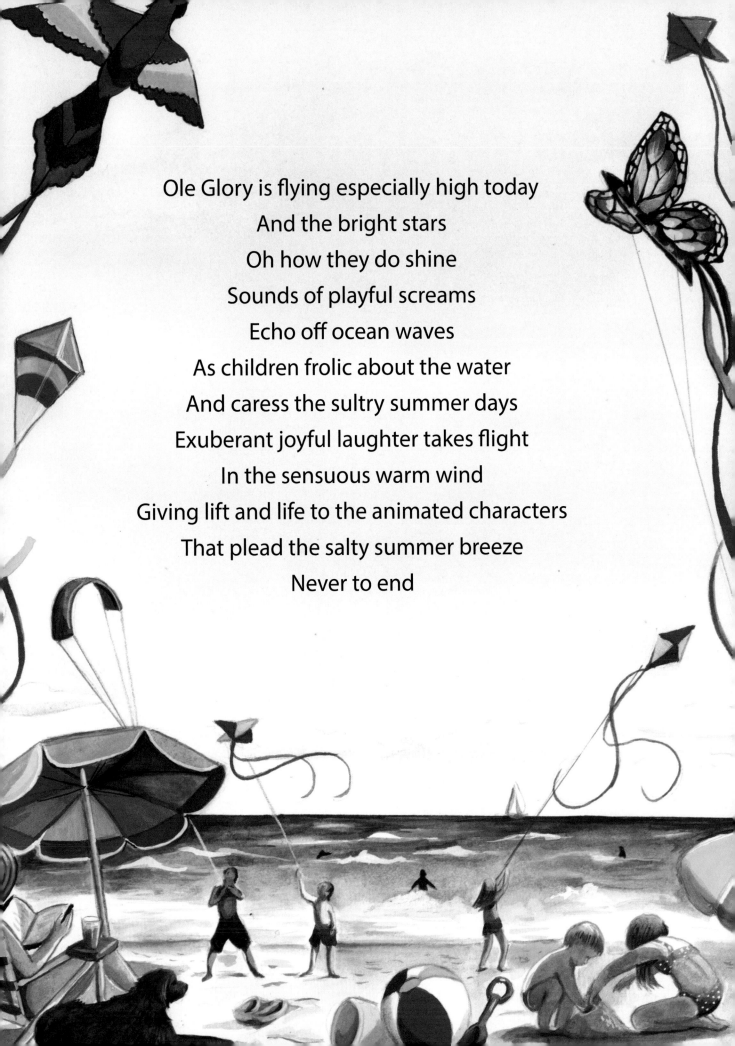

Ole Glory is flying especially high today
And the bright stars
Oh how they do shine
Sounds of playful screams
Echo off ocean waves
As children frolic about the water
And caress the sultry summer days
Exuberant joyful laughter takes flight
In the sensuous warm wind
Giving lift and life to the animated characters
That plead the salty summer breeze
Never to end

The Alabama Beach Mouse

I am a tiny little Beach Mouse
Building fragile castles in the sand
I get help from my friend Gusty the Ghost Crab
He is just the greatest ever at digging
And loves to lend a hand

I much prefer to sleep in days
When the sun shines so hot and bright
But when the cool evening comes
I like to venture out and play
Hiding in the shadows of a silver moonlight
I do so enjoy to hike and climb
Upon the majestic sandy dunes
And ski down the slippery slopes
As the crickets chirp their lullaby tunes

Life was so very peaceful here
That was until the giant buildings came
One time our family home was smushed
Mommy Mouse has not ever been quite the same
Before I had many playmates
That would visit and play with me
But I cannot locate them now
Oh where in the sand could they be

The only life I have ever known
Is on the beautiful
Alabama Gulf Coast
I could never leave here
This my home I cherish the most

Oh well, the sun is dipping down
I am ready to go run and play
Perhaps I will see you out tonight
On the beach near the bay
But be careful where you walk
And take heed to where you stand
Remember I am just a tiny Little Beach Mouse
Building fragile castles in the sand

The Alabama Beach Mouse (Peromyscus poionotus ammobates) is a federally
endangered species that lives along the Alabama Gulf Coast.
The range of the Alabama Beach Mouse
historically included much of the Fort Morgan Peninsula on the
Alabama Gulf Coast and extends from Ono Island to Fort Morgan

Dolphins on Parade

Dad tilted the umbrella slightly
To guide the mid-morning shade

Mom relaxes in her beach chair with binoculars
Awaiting patiently for Dolphins on Parade

Sunshine glistens off the sparkling water

As we bury Dad in the moist cool sand

Lil Sister screams like mad

As Dad grabs her tiny foot with his hidden hand

But where are the Dolphins

It has been three days and they have yet to appear

Perhaps they have moved to a new beach

Or maybe an island far away from here

Oh but we must see them

And I do believe I have a brilliant plan

Let's jump and splash and play in the water

And stir up the golden sand

It seems that they are attracted
To laughter and lively play
We shall sing and dance about in the water
Then surely they will come our way
So we played and rolled in and about
The tumbling ocean waves
Skimming the shoreline on boogie boards
Mom was greatly amazed
And then from out of the blue
Oh what a welcomed surprise
A great gift from the generous sea
A precious image before my salt laden eyes

I counted at least a dozen Dolphins
Perhaps there were many more
Surfing the breaking ocean waves
So very close to the shore
Jumping and flipping and dancing
As great acrobats of the sea
Putting on a mystical performance
The entrancing gracefulness captivated me

Then one congenial dolphin broke pattern
And began to approach so very near
He had a kind gentle smile that seemed to say
Welcome back, sure is good to see you here
I was stunned with his presence
As to stumble upon an old lost friend
And I thought, oh my what a pleasure it is
To find you here once again
Then he swam and resumed position
With the others as they went their way
Flipping and diving, splashing and dancing
As to encore a magnificent play

Even now after so many visits to the Emerald Coast
It seems the grand adventure is never completely made

Until in the presence of friends and family
And a ritual performance
Of Dolphins on Parade

Treasure in The Sand

We walked the bounty laden shoreline
Searching for Treasures in The Sand
Sea shells rich in color, shapes and size
Fill our pink and blue buckets
As we strolled hand in hand

Our imaginations would take us into a world of adventure

As we sailed upon a restless turbulent sea

In a weather worn war ship built for two

I would defend my baby sister

From the infamous pirate Jean Lafitte

He had a black patch over a scarred eye

And a bejeweled sword to show off his rank

With a coarse pirate accent he grumbled

"Give up the lass mate,

Or ye walk the plank"

"Dare ye touch a hair of the maiden's head"

I boldly and fiercely proclaim

I knew what I must do

To make this barbarian refrain

I gave him a blast from my super soaker
And he fell lame to the water face down
My sister started crying so I had to rescue him
Mom would sure be upset if I let Dad drown
Now many delightful seasons have come
Each bringing a tale of its own
I have saved many enchanting sea treasures
And precious memories anew to add to the old
I retreat back with my extended family
To those traditional heart-warming places

And we share infectious laughter
As we usher in a new generation
Of rosy cheeks and glowing faces
And we walk the bounty laden shoreline
Searching for Treasures in The Sand
Sea shells rich in color, shape and size
To fill our pink and blue buckets
As we stroll hand in hand

The Beach Bunny

There is a Beach Bunny who lives
In the Marsh down by the sea
He dines on sea oats and sawgrass

And makes homestead in a hollow cypress knee
He has a collection of sea shells and sand dollars
That he is most greatly fond of
His hobby of beachcombing and collecting
Is a pastime that he really does love

He proudly places them out in his home
For all of his friends to admire and see
And will often tell colorful stories
Of how they came to be
His favorite is of Allie the marsh gator
Who had befriended the Beach Bunny
And invited Him over for surprise stew
But being very clever, quick and witful
The Beach Bunny left Allie the Marsh Gator
A hareless menu

And in the Bunny's haste as he was jumping away
His lucky rabbit foot brushed the sandy ground
A sparkle of gold flashed before his keen eyes
And this is what he had found

A shiny Spanish golden doubloon dated 1492

Perhaps it was left behind by you know who

It's a very attractive and lucky piece

So he carries it wherever he may go

And if you are ever looking for the Beach Bunny

There is just one thing you need to know

There is no place in the whole wide world
That the Beach Bunny would prefer to be
That is why he is fondly known as
The Beach Bunny who lives in the Marsh by the sea

The Sandpiper

The Sandpiper stood firmly
With his back to the wind
No option but to endure

And pray the storm to end
His tiny feet buried in the wet sand
Sink deeper with each gusty blow
How will I ever survive this travesty
Surely life ought not be so cold
The crushing waves were spectacular
As they tumble and thrash the innocent shore

The wind and rain made a haunting cry
The small Sandpiper had not heard before
For he was a juvenile bird
And not yet a cold season had he seen

And this wintry blast
Was a very frightful thing

Birds of a feather, how they flock together
Now I think I understand
As the Sandpipers all huddled around
Protecting each other from the blasting sand

And although he was young and strong
And holding fast to the front line
He felt the weakening of his tiny legs
Afraid he may fall in time
The other birds saw him fragile
And about to give in
They stood to each side and front
To hinder the blusterous wind

Soon the frigid rain stopped
And the furious winds ceased
The birds too exhausted to sing
However so grateful and graciously relieved
It was a most difficult experience
But now I understand
I can weather the most fierce of storms
With friends close at hand
The next year the winter storms came
The Sandpiper stood firmly facing the wind
Enduring and holding fast with confidence
Knowing that the storm would soon end

Cotton Candy Skies

The sunset illuminated pastel colors of the cabanas
As heavenly clouds slowly passed by
The reflection of a red– orange sun from the Gulf
Softly painted a Cotton Candy Sky
Gentle colors that appear brilliant and then slowly dim
An orchestration of light and motion
To bring a glorious day to a fitting end
A taste of God's Glory
A taste of the way things will be
Tis here for us now
If we only have the eyes to see
Alas we much search it out

A precious gift for discerning eyes
Beckoning to be found
Desirous to enrich our lives
And it is a bit perplexing to contemplate
Why some wrestle through life and never realize
That down by the edge of the sea
One can find the most beautiful sunset
And Cotton Candy Skies

Monarchs In November

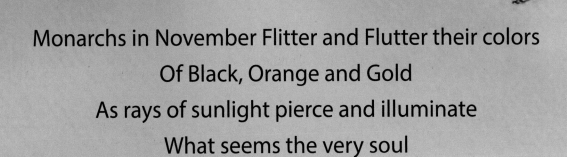

Monarchs in November Flitter and Flutter their colors
Of Black, Orange and Gold
As rays of sunlight pierce and illuminate
What seems the very soul

By instinct and natural call they migrate the island
This most enchanting time of year
While vacationers at home, children in school and
Less speeding windshields to fear

One lone Monarch flies up high
Disappearing in the shadows of the late noon sun

From my balcony
I am captivated by a couple
As they waltz together
They chase and dance about
Like young Love
On the run

Lightly touching down on the white balcony
For rest and a moment of leisure
Then flutter off towards the beach
In search of sweet tropical nectar
This may well be my most favorite time of the year
I do cherish the time that I am granted to be here
To see the Monarchs in November
Flitter and flutter their colors
Of Black , Orange and Gold
As rays of sunlight pierce and illuminate
What seems the very soul

THE MARDI GRAS BOAT PARADE
COMING 2018

Starring all of your favorite animal characters from
TREASURES IN THE SAND and A GULF COAST CHRISTMAS
and introducing a few new cuddly Gulf Coast creatures illustrated by
Tami Curtis (TamiCurtisStudios.com), a Gulf Coast Louisiana native and
highly talented artist.

When visiting Bay St Louis MS, visit Tami's gallery at
112 S. Second St./first floor of the historic Century Hall.

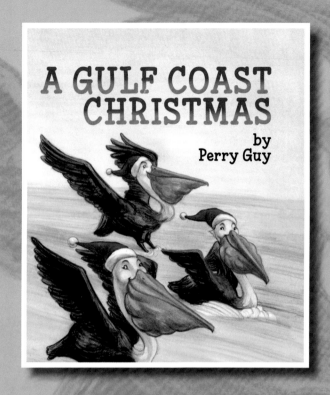

A GULF COAST
CHRISTMAS

A *GULF COAST CHRISTMAS* is bound to become a new Christmas classic that brings together most all the characters of *TREASURES IN THE SAND*, along with some new characters as well, for a fun festive gathering to celebrate the Christmas season .

What a perfect Christmas gift for friends and family.

ORDER YOUR COPIES TODAY

agulfcoastchristmas.com or text me at 251-233-9493
if you prefer to pay by phone.